BUSY BOOKS

SERMON NOTES

FOR KIDS AGES 8-12

MADISON SCHACHT
& DARLENE SCHACHT

Busy Books: Sermon Notes for Kids

Time-Warp Wife Ministries
Suite 5-1377 Border Street
Winnipeg, Manitoba
R3H ON1

Cover design by Darlene Schacht

ISBN 978-0-9780262-8-8

Images from Bigstock.com

Find Time-Warp Wife on the web here:

Blog: TimeWarpWife.com
Facebook: timewarpwife
Twitter: timewarpwife
Pinterest: timewarpwife

WHAT ARE WE DOING HERE?

WHY DO WE GO TO CHURCH?

The Bible says, "And let us consider how we may spur one another on toward love and good deeds, not giving up meeting together, as some are in the habit of doing, but encouraging one another—and all the more as you see the Day approaching."
- Hebrews 10:24&25

We go to church to learn, but we also go to be encouraged and to encourage one another as we grow in faith.

It's more than a building. It's really about the people inside, in fact some churches meet outside, some meet in tents, and others meet in homes. The church is also known as "the body" of Christ. Just like your own body, the parts are attached, and they're all important in their own way. Your brain, your eyes, your mouth, your hands, your feet, your heart, and your skin all work together to serve you, just like members of the church work together to serve God.

And so the church functions best when we work together, to bring glory to God.

WHAT IS OUR RESPONSIBILITY AT CHURCH?

We all know that we need to behave ourselves and listen to the pastor when we're in church, but there's more we can do! By being friendly, saying hello to people, and helping out when we can, we become an encouragement to others and a blessing to God.

HOW SHOULD WE USE THIS BOOK?

Take this book with you to church every week. Don't forget to bring a pen or a pencil with you because you're going to need it to take notes. It would be smart to keep this all together in a bag so it's ready to go when you are.

Do three pages each week. You might be tempted to do more, but don't get ahead of yourself. Good things, like cookies, should be enjoyed in small bites.

Every week you have a chance to earn points. If I was a kid, I'd ask my parents for a little prize if I did well. A gold star? A sticker? A little treat? A new pony? Well... they probably won't go for a pony, but it's worth a try, right?

TODAY'S SERMON

Is about...

God healing in
Uganda.
Tutapana.

Try to get 30 points!

SUNDAY MORNING CHECKLIST

————— give yourself 5 points for each! —————

I prayed when I woke up this morning ☑

I brushed my teeth ☑

I made my bed ☒

I came to church with a good attitude ☑

I said hello to someone when I arrived ☑

I brought my Bible to church ☒

Total . . . . . . ☑

CATCH WORDS

Total _____

Check off any words you hear - Get 3 points for each!

Jesus	●	Heaven	○	Cross	○
God	○	Father	○	Grace	○
Power	○	Son	○	Saved	○
Holy	○	Spirit	○	Forgiveness	○
Pray	●	Bible	○	Amen	○
Love	○	Faith	○	Joy	○
Worship	●	Disciples	○	Peace	○

My Favorite Song Today _____

Use this space to mark down things you didn't understand or questions you might have.

TODAY'S SERMON

Is about...

Weakness and the
Power of Christ

Try to get
30 points!

SUNDAY MORNING CHECKLIST

give yourself 5 points for each!

I prayed when I woke up this morning

I brushed my teeth

I made my bed

I came to church with a good attitude

I said hello to someone when I arrived

I brought my Bible to church

Total . . . . . .

CATCH WORDS

Total _____

Check off any words you hear - Get 3 points for each!

Jesus	⊘	Heaven	○	Cross	○
God	○	Father	○	Grace	⊘
Power	○	Son	○	Saved	○
Holy	○	Spirit	○	Forgiveness	○
Pray	○	Bible	○	Amen	⊘
Love	○	Faith	○	Joy	○
Worship	○	Disciples	○	Peace	○

My Favorite Song Today _____

Use this space to mark down things you didn't understand or questions you might have.

This Week I'll Pray For...

Did you read your Bible this week? If you did, give yourself 10 points!

Extra notes or doodles go here --->

Tally up your points!

TODAY'S SERMON
Is about...

_____

_____

_____

_____

_____

_____

_____

Try to get 30 points!

SUNDAY MORNING CHECKLIST
_____ give yourself 5 points for each! _____

I prayed when I woke up this morning ☑

I brushed my teeth ☑

I made my bed ☒

I came to church with a good attitude ☑

I said hello to someone when I arrived ☑

I brought my Bible to church ☑

Total . . . . . . ☑

mommy loves Blake

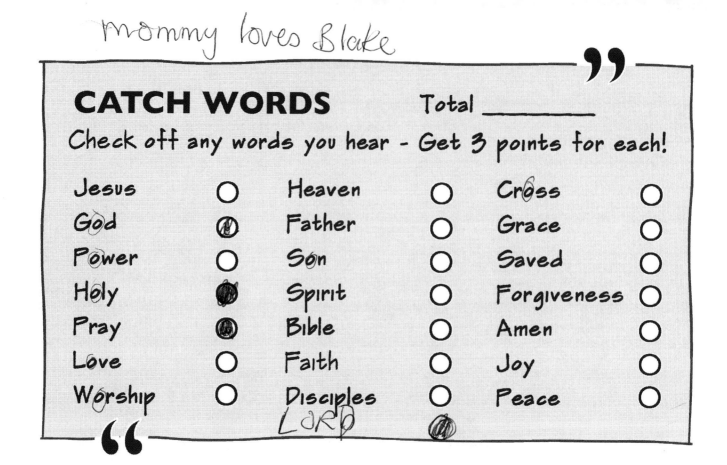

CATCH WORDS   Total _____

Check off any words you hear - Get 3 points for each!

Jesus	○	Heaven	○	Cross	○
God	◉	Father	○	Grace	○
Power	○	Son	○	Saved	○
Holy	●	Spirit	○	Forgiveness	○
Pray	●	Bible	○	Amen	○
Love	○	Faith	○	Joy	○
Worship	○	Disciples	○	Peace	○
		LORD	◉		

My Favorite Song Today _____

_____
_____
_____

Use this space
to mark down
things you didn't
understand or
questions you
might have.

This Week I'll Pray For...

Beeh hels weel char

Did you read your Bible this week?
If you did, give yourself 10 points!

Extra notes
or doodles go
here --->

Tally up
your
points!

TODAY'S SERMON

Is about...

_____
_____
_____
_____
_____
_____
_____

DATE
_____

Try to get 30 points!

SUNDAY MORNING CHECKLIST

_____ give yourself 5 points for each! _____

I prayed when I woke up this morning ☐

I brushed my teeth ☐

I made my bed ☐

I came to church with a good attitude ☐

I said hello to someone when I arrived ☐

I brought my Bible to church ☐

Total . . . . . . ☐

CATCH WORDS

Total _____

Check off any words you hear - Get 3 points for each!

Jesus	○	Heaven	○	Cross	○
God	○	Father	○	Grace	○
Power	○	Son	○	Saved	○
Holy	○	Spirit	○	Forgiveness	○
Pray	○	Bible	○	Amen	○
Love	○	Faith	○	Joy	○
Worship	○	Disciples	○	Peace	○

My Favorite Song Today _____

Use this space to mark down things you didn't understand or questions you might have.

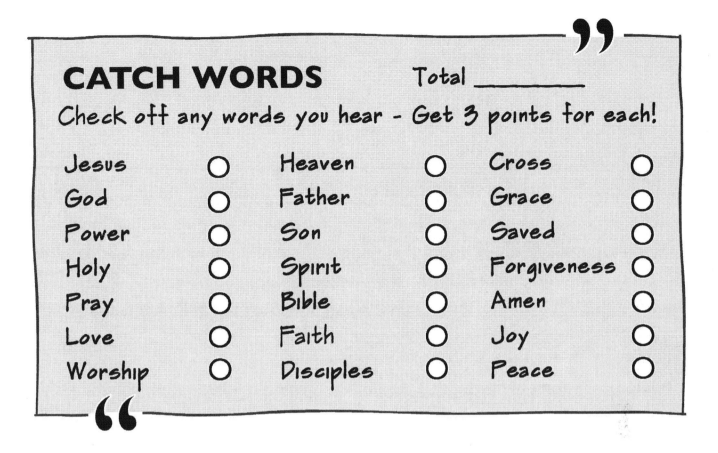

TODAY'S SERMON

Is about...

_____

_____

_____

_____

_____

_____

_____

DATE

_____

Try to get 30 points!

SUNDAY MORNING CHECKLIST

give yourself 5 points for each!

I prayed when I woke up this morning ☐

I brushed my teeth ☐

I made my bed ☐

I came to church with a good attitude ☐

I said hello to someone when I arrived ☐

I brought my Bible to church ☐

Total . . . . . . ☐

CATCH WORDS

Total _____

Check off any words you hear - Get 3 points for each!

Jesus	○	Heaven	○	Cross	○
God	○	Father	○	Grace	○
Power	○	Son	○	Saved	○
Holy	○	Spirit	○	Forgiveness	○
Pray	○	Bible	○	Amen	○
Love	○	Faith	○	Joy	○
Worship	○	Disciples	○	Peace	○

My Favorite Song Today _____

Use this space to mark down things you didn't understand or questions you might have.

TODAY'S SERMON
Is about...

_____
_____
_____
_____
_____
_____
_____

DATE
_____

Try to get 30 points!

SUNDAY MORNING CHECKLIST
_____ give yourself 5 points for each! _____

I prayed when I woke up this morning ☐

I brushed my teeth ☐

I made my bed ☐

I came to church with a good attitude ☐

I said hello to someone when I arrived ☐

I brought my Bible to church ☐

Total . . . . . . ☐

CATCH WORDS

Total _____

Check off any words you hear - Get 3 points for each!

Jesus	⭘	Heaven	⭘	Cross	⭘
God	⭘	Father	⭘	Grace	⭘
Power	⭘	Son	⭘	Saved	⭘
Holy	⭘	Spirit	⭘	Forgiveness	⭘
Pray	⭘	Bible	⭘	Amen	⭘
Love	⭘	Faith	⭘	Joy	⭘
Worship	⭘	Disciples	⭘	Peace	⭘

My Favorite Song Today _____

Use this space to mark down things you didn't understand or questions you might have.

TODAY'S SERMON

Is about...

_____

_____

_____

_____

_____

_____

_____

DATE

_____

Try to get 30 points!

SUNDAY MORNING CHECKLIST

_____ give yourself 5 points for each! _____

I prayed when I woke up this morning ☐

I brushed my teeth ☐

I made my bed ☐

I came to church with a good attitude ☐

I said hello to someone when I arrived ☐

I brought my Bible to church ☐

Total . . . . . . ☐

CATCH WORDS

Total _____

Check off any words you hear - Get 3 points for each!

Jesus	○	Heaven	○	Cross	○
God	○	Father	○	Grace	○
Power	○	Son	○	Saved	○
Holy	○	Spirit	○	Forgiveness	○
Pray	○	Bible	○	Amen	○
Love	○	Faith	○	Joy	○
Worship	○	Disciples	○	Peace	○

My Favorite Song Today _____

_____

_____

_____

Use this space to mark down things you didn't understand or questions you might have.

TODAY'S SERMON

Is about...

_____

_____

_____

_____

_____

_____

_____

DATE

_____

Try to get 30 points!

SUNDAY MORNING CHECKLIST

_____ give yourself 5 points for each! _____

I prayed when I woke up this morning ☐

I brushed my teeth ☐

I made my bed ☐

I came to church with a good attitude ☐

I said hello to someone when I arrived ☐

I brought my Bible to church ☐

Total . . . . . . ☐

CATCH WORDS

Total _____

Check off any words you hear - Get 3 points for each!

Jesus ○	Heaven ○	Cross ○
God ○	Father ○	Grace ○
Power ○	Son ○	Saved ○
Holy ○	Spirit ○	Forgiveness ○
Pray ○	Bible ○	Amen ○
Love ○	Faith ○	Joy ○
Worship ○	Disciples ○	Peace ○

My Favorite Song Today _____

Use this space to mark down things you didn't understand or questions you might have.

TODAY'S SERMON

Is about...

_____

_____

_____

_____

_____

_____

_____

DATE

_____

Try to get 30 points!

SUNDAY MORNING CHECKLIST

_____ give yourself 5 points for each! _____

I prayed when I woke up this morning ☐

I brushed my teeth ☐

I made my bed ☐

I came to church with a good attitude ☐

I said hello to someone when I arrived ☐

I brought my Bible to church ☐

Total . . . . . . ☐

CATCH WORDS

Total _____

Check off any words you hear - Get 3 points for each!

Jesus ○	Heaven ○	Cross ○
God ○	Father ○	Grace ○
Power ○	Son ○	Saved ○
Holy ○	Spirit ○	Forgiveness ○
Pray ○	Bible ○	Amen ○
Love ○	Faith ○	Joy ○
Worship ○	Disciples ○	Peace ○

My Favorite Song Today _____

Use this space to mark down things you didn't understand or questions you might have.

TODAY'S SERMON

Is about...

_____

_____

_____

_____

_____

_____

_____

DATE

_____

Try to get 30 points!

SUNDAY MORNING CHECKLIST

————— give yourself 5 points for each! —————

I prayed when I woke up this morning ☐

I brushed my teeth ☐

I made my bed ☐

I came to church with a good attitude ☐

I said hello to someone when I arrived ☐

I brought my Bible to church ☐

Total . . . . . ☐

CATCH WORDS

Total _____

Check off any words you hear - Get 3 points for each!

Jesus ⚪	Heaven ⚪	Cross ⚪
God ⚪	Father ⚪	Grace ⚪
Power ⚪	Son ⚪	Saved ⚪
Holy ⚪	Spirit ⚪	Forgiveness ⚪
Pray ⚪	Bible ⚪	Amen ⚪
Love ⚪	Faith ⚪	Joy ⚪
Worship ⚪	Disciples ⚪	Peace ⚪

My Favorite Song Today _____

Use this space to mark down things you didn't understand or questions you might have.

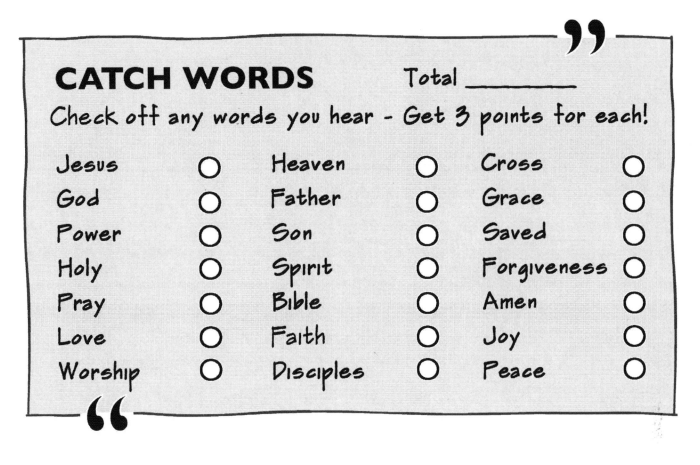

TODAY'S SERMON

Is about...

_____

_____

_____

_____

_____

_____

_____

DATE

_____

Try to get 30 points!

SUNDAY MORNING CHECKLIST

_____ give yourself 5 points for each! _____

I prayed when I woke up this morning ☐

I brushed my teeth ☐

I made my bed ☐

I came to church with a good attitude ☐

I said hello to someone when I arrived ☐

I brought my Bible to church ☐

Total . . . . . . ☐

CATCH WORDS

Total _____

Check off any words you hear - Get 3 points for each!

Jesus	○	Heaven	○	Cross	○
God	○	Father	○	Grace	○
Power	○	Son	○	Saved	○
Holy	○	Spirit	○	Forgiveness	○
Pray	○	Bible	○	Amen	○
Love	○	Faith	○	Joy	○
Worship	○	Disciples	○	Peace	○

My Favorite Song Today _____

_____

_____

_____

Use this space to mark down things you didn't understand or questions you might have.

TODAY'S SERMON
Is about...

_____
_____
_____
_____
_____
_____
_____

DATE
_____

Try to get 30 points!

SUNDAY MORNING CHECKLIST
_____ give yourself 5 points for each! _____

I prayed when I woke up this morning ☐

I brushed my teeth ☐

I made my bed ☐

I came to church with a good attitude ☐

I said hello to someone when I arrived ☐

I brought my Bible to church ☐

Total . . . . . . ☐

CATCH WORDS

Total _____

Check off any words you hear - Get 3 points for each!

Jesus	○	Heaven	○	Cross	○
God	○	Father	○	Grace	○
Power	○	Son	○	Saved	○
Holy	○	Spirit	○	Forgiveness	○
Pray	○	Bible	○	Amen	○
Love	○	Faith	○	Joy	○
Worship	○	Disciples	○	Peace	○

My Favorite Song Today _____

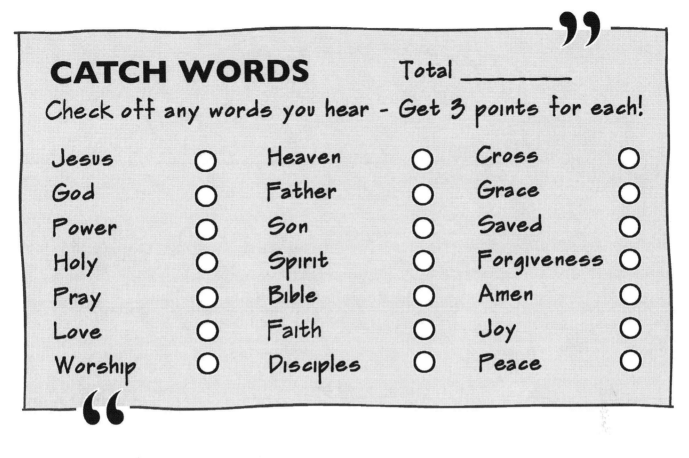

Use this space to mark down things you didn't understand or questions you might have.

TODAY'S SERMON

Is about...

_____
_____
_____
_____
_____
_____
_____

DATE

_____

Try to get 30 points!

SUNDAY MORNING CHECKLIST

_____ give yourself 5 points for each! _____

I prayed when I woke up this morning ☐

I brushed my teeth ☐

I made my bed ☐

I came to church with a good attitude ☐

I said hello to someone when I arrived ☐

I brought my Bible to church ☐

Total . . . . . . ☐

CATCH WORDS

Total _____

Check off any words you hear - Get 3 points for each!

Jesus	◯	Heaven	◯	Cross	◯
God	◯	Father	◯	Grace	◯
Power	◯	Son	◯	Saved	◯
Holy	◯	Spirit	◯	Forgiveness	◯
Pray	◯	Bible	◯	Amen	◯
Love	◯	Faith	◯	Joy	◯
Worship	◯	Disciples	◯	Peace	◯

My Favorite Song Today _____

_____

_____

_____

Use this space to mark down things you didn't understand or questions you might have.

TODAY'S SERMON

Is about...

_____
_____
_____
_____
_____
_____
_____

DATE
_____

Try to get 30 points!

SUNDAY MORNING CHECKLIST

_____ give yourself 5 points for each! _____

I prayed when I woke up this morning ☐

I brushed my teeth ☐

I made my bed ☐

I came to church with a good attitude ☐

I said hello to someone when I arrived ☐

I brought my Bible to church ☐

Total . . . . . . ☐

CATCH WORDS   Total _____

Check off any words you hear - Get 3 points for each!

Jesus	○	Heaven	○	Cross	○
God	○	Father	○	Grace	○
Power	○	Son	○	Saved	○
Holy	○	Spirit	○	Forgiveness	○
Pray	○	Bible	○	Amen	○
Love	○	Faith	○	Joy	○
Worship	○	Disciples	○	Peace	○

My Favorite Song Today _____

_____

_____

_____

Use this space to mark down things you didn't understand or questions you might have.

TODAY'S SERMON

Is about...

_____

_____

_____

_____

_____

_____

_____

DATE

_____

Try to get 30 points!

SUNDAY MORNING CHECKLIST

_____ give yourself 5 points for each! _____

I prayed when I woke up this morning

I brushed my teeth

I made my bed

I came to church with a good attitude

I said hello to someone when I arrived

I brought my Bible to church

Total . . . . . .

CATCH WORDS

Total _____

Check off any words you hear - Get 3 points for each!

Jesus	◯	Heaven	◯	Cross	◯
God	◯	Father	◯	Grace	◯
Power	◯	Son	◯	Saved	◯
Holy	◯	Spirit	◯	Forgiveness	◯
Pray	◯	Bible	◯	Amen	◯
Love	◯	Faith	◯	Joy	◯
Worship	◯	Disciples	◯	Peace	◯

My Favorite Song Today _____

_____

_____

_____

Use this space to mark down things you didn't understand or questions you might have.

TODAY'S SERMON

Is about...

_____

_____

_____

_____

_____

_____

_____

DATE
_____

Try to get 30 points!

SUNDAY MORNING CHECKLIST
_____ give yourself 5 points for each! _____

I prayed when I woke up this morning ☐

I brushed my teeth ☐

I made my bed ☐

I came to church with a good attitude ☐

I said hello to someone when I arrived ☐

I brought my Bible to church ☐

Total . . . . . . ☐

CATCH WORDS

Total _____

Check off any words you hear - Get 3 points for each!

Jesus	○	Heaven	○	Cross	○
God	○	Father	○	Grace	○
Power	○	Son	○	Saved	○
Holy	○	Spirit	○	Forgiveness	○
Pray	○	Bible	○	Amen	○
Love	○	Faith	○	Joy	○
Worship	○	Disciples	○	Peace	○

My Favorite Song Today _____

Use this space to mark down things you didn't understand or questions you might have.

TODAY'S SERMON
Is about...

_____
_____
_____
_____
_____
_____
_____

DATE
_____

Try to get 30 points!

SUNDAY MORNING CHECKLIST
_____ give yourself 5 points for each! _____

I prayed when I woke up this morning ☐

I brushed my teeth ☐

I made my bed ☐

I came to church with a good attitude ☐

I said hello to someone when I arrived ☐

I brought my Bible to church ☐

Total . . . . . . ☐

CATCH WORDS

Total _____

Check off any words you hear - Get 3 points for each!

Jesus	○	Heaven	○	Cross	○
God	○	Father	○	Grace	○
Power	○	Son	○	Saved	○
Holy	○	Spirit	○	Forgiveness	○
Pray	○	Bible	○	Amen	○
Love	○	Faith	○	Joy	○
Worship	○	Disciples	○	Peace	○

My Favorite Song Today _____

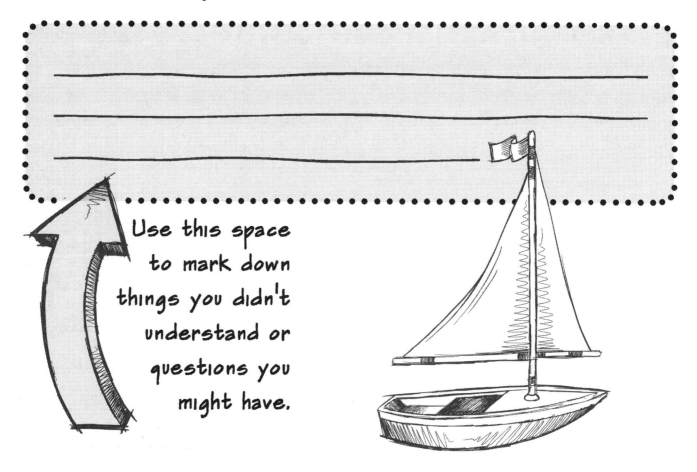

Use this space to mark down things you didn't understand or questions you might have.

TODAY'S SERMON

Is about...

_____

_____

_____

_____

_____

_____

_____

DATE

_____

Try to get 30 points!

SUNDAY MORNING CHECKLIST

_____ give yourself 5 points for each! _____

I prayed when I woke up this morning ☐

I brushed my teeth ☐

I made my bed ☐

I came to church with a good attitude ☐

I said hello to someone when I arrived ☐

I brought my Bible to church ☐

Total . . . . . . ☐

CATCH WORDS

Total _____

Check off any words you hear - Get 3 points for each!

Jesus	○	Heaven	○	Cross	○
God	○	Father	○	Grace	○
Power	○	Son	○	Saved	○
Holy	○	Spirit	○	Forgiveness	○
Pray	○	Bible	○	Amen	○
Love	○	Faith	○	Joy	○
Worship	○	Disciples	○	Peace	○

My Favorite Song Today _____

Use this space to mark down things you didn't understand or questions you might have.

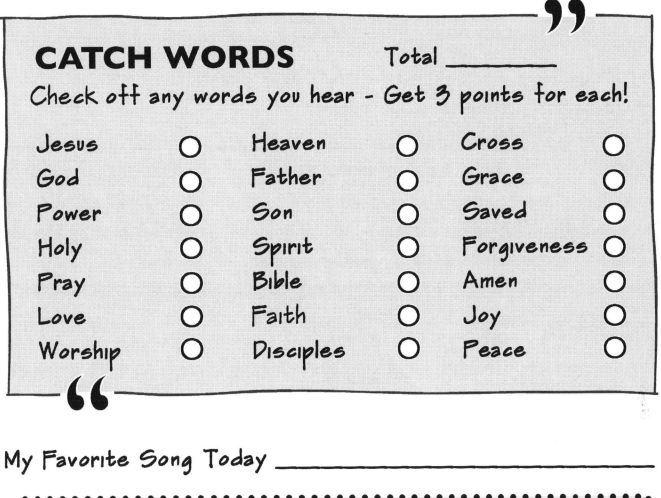

TODAY'S SERMON

Is about...

_____
_____
_____
_____
_____
_____
_____

DATE
_____

Try to get 30 points!

SUNDAY MORNING CHECKLIST

_____ give yourself 5 points for each! _____

I prayed when I woke up this morning ☐

I brushed my teeth ☐

I made my bed ☐

I came to church with a good attitude ☐

I said hello to someone when I arrived ☐

I brought my Bible to church ☐

Total . . . . . . ☐

CATCH WORDS

Total _____

Check off any words you hear - Get 3 points for each!

Jesus	⭘	Heaven	⭘	Cross	⭘
God	⭘	Father	⭘	Grace	⭘
Power	⭘	Son	⭘	Saved	⭘
Holy	⭘	Spirit	⭘	Forgiveness	⭘
Pray	⭘	Bible	⭘	Amen	⭘
Love	⭘	Faith	⭘	Joy	⭘
Worship	⭘	Disciples	⭘	Peace	⭘

My Favorite Song Today _____

_____

_____

_____

Use this space to mark down things you didn't understand or questions you might have.

TODAY'S SERMON

Is about...

_____
_____
_____
_____
_____
_____
_____

DATE

_____

Try to get 30 points!

SUNDAY MORNING CHECKLIST

_____ give yourself 5 points for each! _____

I prayed when I woke up this morning ☐

I brushed my teeth ☐

I made my bed ☐

I came to church with a good attitude ☐

I said hello to someone when I arrived ☐

I brought my Bible to church ☐

Total . . . . . . ☐

CATCH WORDS

Total _____

Check off any words you hear - Get 3 points for each!

Jesus	⭕	Heaven	⭕	Cross	⭕
God	⭕	Father	⭕	Grace	⭕
Power	⭕	Son	⭕	Saved	⭕
Holy	⭕	Spirit	⭕	Forgiveness	⭕
Pray	⭕	Bible	⭕	Amen	⭕
Love	⭕	Faith	⭕	Joy	⭕
Worship	⭕	Disciples	⭕	Peace	⭕

My Favorite Song Today _____

Use this space to mark down things you didn't understand or questions you might have.

TODAY'S SERMON

Is about...

_____
_____
_____
_____
_____
_____
_____

DATE

_____

Try to get 30 points!

SUNDAY MORNING CHECKLIST

give yourself 5 points for each!

I prayed when I woke up this morning ☐

I brushed my teeth ☐

I made my bed ☐

I came to church with a good attitude ☐

I said hello to someone when I arrived ☐

I brought my Bible to church ☐

Total . . . . . . ☐

CATCH WORDS

Total _____

check off any words you hear - Get 3 points for each!

Jesus	○	Heaven	○	Cross	○
God	○	Father	○	Grace	○
Power	○	Son	○	Saved	○
Holy	○	Spirit	○	Forgiveness	○
Pray	○	Bible	○	Amen	○
Love	○	Love	○	Joy	○
Worship	○	Disciples	○	Peace	○

My Favorite Song Today _____

_____

_____

_____

Use this space to mark down things you didn't understand or questions you might have.

TODAY'S SERMON

Is about...

_____

_____

_____

_____

_____

_____

_____

DATE

_____

Try to get 30 points!

SUNDAY MORNING CHECKLIST

_____ give yourself 5 points for each! _____

I prayed when I woke up this morning ☐

I brushed my teeth ☐

I made my bed ☐

I came to church with a good attitude ☐

I said hello to someone when I arrived ☐

I brought my Bible to church ☐

Total . . . . . . ☐

CATCH WORDS

Total _____

Check off any words you hear - Get 3 points for each!

Jesus	○	Heaven	○	Cross	○
God	○	Father	○	Grace	○
Power	○	Son	○	Saved	○
Holy	○	Spirit	○	Forgiveness	○
Pray	○	Bible	○	Amen	○
Love	○	Faith	○	Joy	○
Worship	○	Disciples	○	Peace	○

My Favorite Song Today _____

_____

_____

_____

Use this space to mark down things you didn't understand or questions you might have.

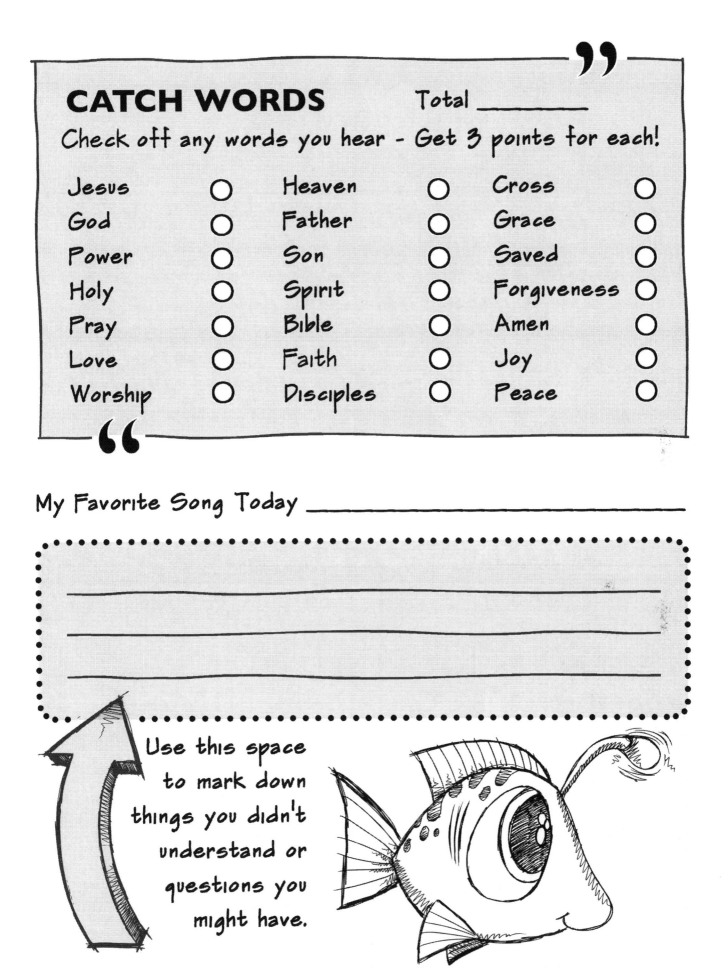

TODAY'S SERMON

Is about...

_____

_____

_____

_____

_____

_____

_____

DATE

_____

Try to get 30 points!

SUNDAY MORNING CHECKLIST

—— give yourself 5 points for each! ——

I prayed when I woke up this morning ☐

I brushed my teeth ☐

I made my bed ☐

I came to church with a good attitude ☐

I said hello to someone when I arrived ☐

I brought my Bible to church ☐

Total . . . . . . ☐

CATCH WORDS

Total _____

Check off any words you hear - Get 3 points for each!

Jesus	○	Heaven	○	Cross	○
God	○	Father	○	Grace	○
Power	○	Son	○	Saved	○
Holy	○	Spirit	○	Forgiveness	○
Pray	○	Bible	○	Amen	○
Love	○	Faith	○	Joy	○
Worship	○	Disciples	○	Peace	○

My Favorite Song Today _____

Use this space to mark down things you didn't understand or questions you might have.

TODAY'S SERMON
Is about...

_____
_____
_____
_____
_____
_____
_____

DATE
_____

Try to get 30 points!

SUNDAY MORNING CHECKLIST
_____ give yourself 5 points for each! _____

I prayed when I woke up this morning ☐

I brushed my teeth ☐

I made my bed ☐

I came to church with a good attitude ☐

I said hello to someone when I arrived ☐

I brought my Bible to church ☐

Total . . . . . ☐

CATCH WORDS

Total _____

Check off any words you hear - Get 3 points for each!

Jesus	◯	Heaven	◯	Cross	◯
God	◯	Father	◯	Grace	◯
Power	◯	Son	◯	Saved	◯
Holy	◯	Spirit	◯	Forgiveness	◯
Pray	◯	Bible	◯	Amen	◯
Love	◯	Faith	◯	Joy	◯
Worship	◯	Disciples	◯	Peace	◯

My Favorite Song Today _____

Use this space to mark down things you didn't understand or questions you might have.

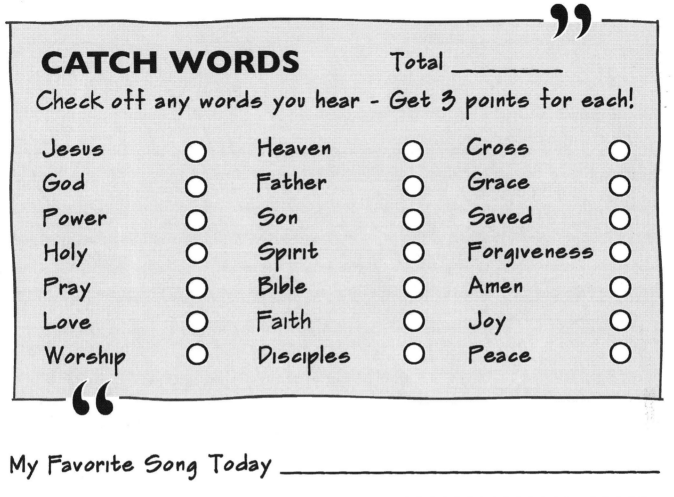

TODAY'S SERMON

Is about...

_____
_____
_____
_____
_____
_____
_____

DATE

_____

Try to get 30 points!

SUNDAY MORNING CHECKLIST

——— give yourself 5 points for each! ———

I prayed when I woke up this morning ☐

I brushed my teeth ☐

I made my bed ☐

I came to church with a good attitude ☐

I said hello to someone when I arrived ☐

I brought my Bible to church ☐

Total . . . . . . ☐

CATCH WORDS

Total _____

Check off any words you hear - Get 3 points for each!

Jesus	○	Heaven	○	Cross	○
God	○	Father	○	Grace	○
Power	○	Son	○	Saved	○
Holy	○	Spirit	○	Forgiveness	○
Pray	○	Bible	○	Amen	○
Love	○	Faith	○	Joy	○
Worship	○	Disciples	○	Peace	○

My Favorite Song Today _____

Use this space to mark down things you didn't understand or questions you might have.

TODAY'S SERMON

Is about...

_____
_____
_____
_____
_____
_____
_____

DATE

_____

Try to get 30 points!

SUNDAY MORNING CHECKLIST

_____ give yourself 5 points for each! _____

I prayed when I woke up this morning ☐

I brushed my teeth ☐

I made my bed ☐

I came to church with a good attitude ☐

I said hello to someone when I arrived ☐

I brought my Bible to church ☐

Total . . . . . . ☐

CATCH WORDS

Total _____

Check off any words you hear - Get 3 points for each!

Jesus	○	Heaven	○	Cross	○
God	○	Father	○	Grace	○
Power	○	Son	○	Saved	○
Holy	○	Spirit	○	Forgiveness	○
Pray	○	Bible	○	Amen	○
Love	○	Faith	○	Joy	○
Worship	○	Disciples	○	Peace	○

My Favorite Song Today _____

_____

_____

_____

Use this space to mark down things you didn't understand or questions you might have.

TODAY'S SERMON

Is about...

_____
_____
_____
_____
_____
_____
_____

DATE

_____

Try to get 30 points!

SUNDAY MORNING CHECKLIST

_____ give yourself 5 points for each! _____

I prayed when I woke up this morning ☐

I brushed my teeth ☐

I made my bed ☐

I came to church with a good attitude ☐

I said hello to someone when I arrived ☐

I brought my Bible to church ☐

Total . . . . . . ☐

CATCH WORDS

Total _____

Check off any words you hear - Get 3 points for each!

Jesus	◯	Heaven	◯	Cross	◯
God	◯	Father	◯	Grace	◯
Power	◯	Son	◯	Saved	◯
Holy	◯	Spirit	◯	Forgiveness	◯
Pray	◯	Bible	◯	Amen	◯
Love	◯	Faith	◯	Joy	◯
Worship	◯	Disciples	◯	Peace	◯

My Favorite Song Today _____

_____
_____
_____

Use this space to mark down things you didn't understand or questions you might have.

TODAY'S SERMON

Is about...

REAJANO
MOM

Try to get 30 points!

SUNDAY MORNING CHECKLIST

give yourself 5 points for each!

I prayed when I woke up this morning ✓

I brushed my teeth ✓

I made my bed ✓

I came to church with a good attitude ✓

I said hello to someone when I arrived ✓

I brought my Bible to church ✓

Total . . . . . . ✓

CATCH WORDS

Total _____

Check off any words you hear - Get 3 points for each!

Jesus	◯	Heaven	◯	Cross	◯
God	◯	Father	◯	Grace	◯
Power	◯	Son	◯	Saved	◯
Holy	◯	Spirit	◯	Forgiveness	◯
Pray	◯	Bible	◯	Amen	◯
Love	◯	Faith	◯	Joy	◯
Worship	◯	Disciples	◯	Peace	◯

My Favorite Song Today _____

_____

_____

_____

Use this space to mark down things you didn't understand or questions you might have.

TODAY'S SERMON

Is about...

_____
_____
_____
_____
_____
_____
_____

DATE
_____

Try to get 30 points!

SUNDAY MORNING CHECKLIST

_____ give yourself 5 points for each! _____

I prayed when I woke up this morning ☐

I brushed my teeth ☐

I made my bed ☐

I came to church with a good attitude ☐

I said hello to someone when I arrived ☐

I brought my Bible to church ☐

Total . . . . . . ☐

CATCH WORDS

Total _____

Check off any words you hear - Get 3 points for each!

Jesus	○	Heaven	○	Cross	○
God	○	Father	○	Grace	○
Power	○	Son	○	Saved	○
Holy	○	Spirit	○	Forgiveness	○
Pray	○	Bible	○	Amen	○
Love	○	Faith	○	Joy	○
Worship	○	Disciples	○	Peace	○

My Favorite Song Today _____

_____

_____

_____

Use this space to mark down things you didn't understand or questions you might have.

TODAY'S SERMON

Is about...

_____

_____

_____

_____

_____

_____

_____

DATE

_____

Try to get 30 points!

SUNDAY MORNING CHECKLIST

_____ give yourself 5 points for each! _____

I prayed when I woke up this morning ☐

I brushed my teeth ☐

I made my bed ☐

I came to church with a good attitude ☐

I said hello to someone when I arrived ☐

I brought my Bible to church ☐

Total . . . . . . ☐

CATCH WORDS

Total _____

Check off any words you hear - Get 3 points for each!

Jesus	◯	Heaven	◯	Cross	◯
God	◯	Father	◯	Grace	◯
Power	◯	Son	◯	Saved	◯
Holy	◯	Spirit	◯	Forgiveness	◯
Pray	◯	Bible	◯	Amen	◯
Love	◯	Faith	◯	Joy	◯
Worship	◯	Disciples	◯	Peace	◯

My Favorite Song Today _____

_____
_____
_____

Use this space to mark down things you didn't understand or questions you might have.

TODAY'S SERMON

Is about...

_____
_____
_____
_____
_____
_____
_____

DATE
_____

Try to get 30 points!

SUNDAY MORNING CHECKLIST

_____ give yourself 5 points for each! _____

I prayed when I woke up this morning ☐

I brushed my teeth ☐

I made my bed ☐

I came to church with a good attitude ☐

I said hello to someone when I arrived ☐

I brought my Bible to church ☐

Total . . . . . . ☐

CATCH WORDS
Total _____

Check off any words you hear - Get 3 points for each!

Jesus	○	Heaven	○	Cross	○
God	○	Father	○	Grace	○
Power	○	Son	○	Saved	○
Holy	○	Spirit	○	Forgiveness	○
Pray	○	Bible	○	Amen	○
Love	○	Faith	○	Joy	○
Worship	○	Disciples	○	Peace	○

My Favorite Song Today _____

_____

_____

_____

Use this space to mark down things you didn't understand or questions you might have.

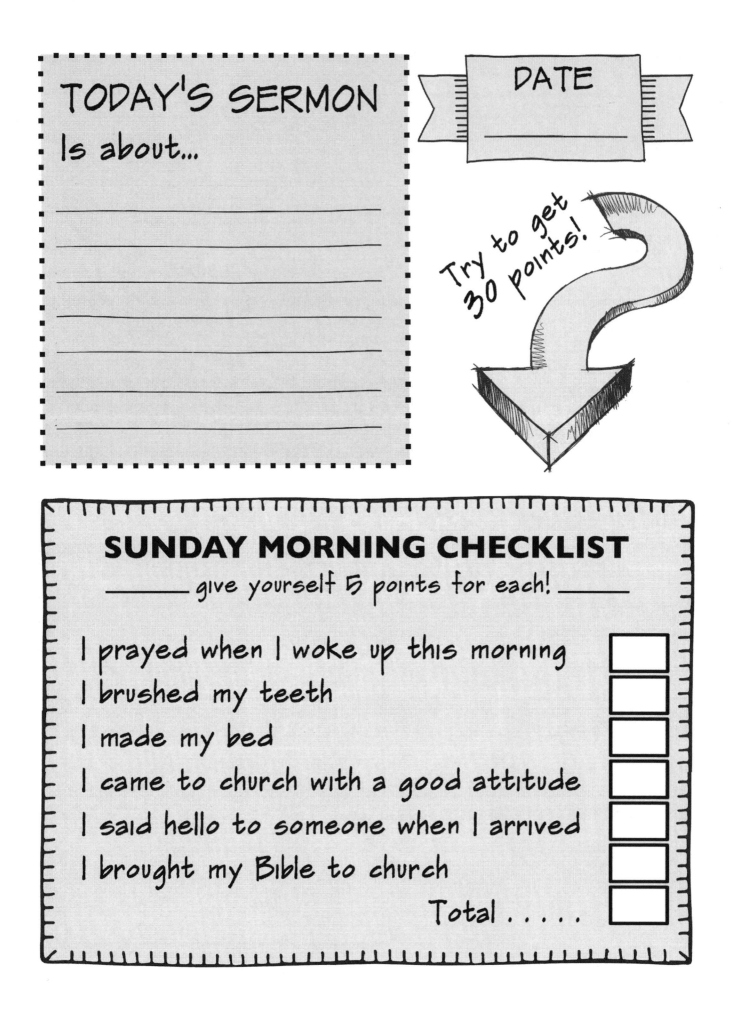

TODAY'S SERMON
Is about...

_____

_____

_____

_____

_____

_____

_____

DATE
_____

Try to get 30 points!

SUNDAY MORNING CHECKLIST
_____ give yourself 5 points for each! _____

I prayed when I woke up this morning

I brushed my teeth

I made my bed

I came to church with a good attitude

I said hello to someone when I arrived

I brought my Bible to church

Total . . . . . .

CATCH WORDS

Total _____

Check off any words you hear - Get 3 points for each!

Jesus	○	Heaven	○	Cross	○
God	○	Father	○	Grace	○
Power	○	Son	○	Saved	○
Holy	○	Spirit	○	Forgiveness	○
Pray	○	Bible	○	Amen	○
Love	○	Faith	○	Joy	○
Worship	○	Disciples	○	Peace	○

My Favorite Song Today _____

Use this space to mark down things you didn't understand or questions you might have.

TODAY'S SERMON

Is about...

_____
_____
_____
_____
_____
_____
_____

DATE

_____

Try to get 30 points!

SUNDAY MORNING CHECKLIST

_____ give yourself 5 points for each! _____

I prayed when I woke up this morning ☐

I brushed my teeth ☐

I made my bed ☐

I came to church with a good attitude ☐

I said hello to someone when I arrived ☐

I brought my Bible to church ☐

Total . . . . . . ☐

CATCH WORDS

Total _____

Check off any words you hear - Get 3 points for each!

Jesus	○	Heaven	○	Cross	○
God	○	Father	○	Grace	○
Power	○	Son	○	Saved	○
Holy	○	Spirit	○	Forgiveness	○
Pray	○	Bible	○	Amen	○
Love	○	Faith	○	Joy	○
Worship	○	Disciples	○	Peace	○

My Favorite Song Today _____

_____
_____
_____

Use this space to mark down things you didn't understand or questions you might have.

TODAY'S SERMON

Is about...

_____
_____
_____
_____
_____
_____
_____

DATE
_____

Try to get 30 points!

SUNDAY MORNING CHECKLIST

give yourself 5 points for each!

I prayed when I woke up this morning ☐

I brushed my teeth ☐

I made my bed ☐

I came to church with a good attitude ☐

I said hello to someone when I arrived ☐

I brought my Bible to church ☐

Total . . . . . . ☐

CATCH WORDS

Total _____

Check off any words you hear - Get 3 points for each!

Jesus	○	Heaven	○	Cross	○
God	○	Father	○	Grace	○
Power	○	Son	○	Saved	○
Holy	○	Spirit	○	Forgiveness	○
Pray	○	Bible	○	Amen	○
Love	○	Faith	○	Joy	○
Worship	○	Disciples	○	Peace	○

My Favorite Song Today _____

_____
_____
_____

Use this space to mark down things you didn't understand or questions you might have.

TODAY'S SERMON

Is about...

_____
_____
_____
_____
_____
_____
_____

DATE
_____

Try to get 30 points!

SUNDAY MORNING CHECKLIST

_____ give yourself 5 points for each! _____

I prayed when I woke up this morning ☐

I brushed my teeth ☐

I made my bed ☐

I came to church with a good attitude ☐

I said hello to someone when I arrived ☐

I brought my Bible to church ☐

Total . . . . . . ☐

CATCH WORDS

Total _____

Check off any words you hear - Get 3 points for each!

Jesus	○	Heaven	○	Cross	○
God	○	Father	○	Grace	○
Power	○	Son	○	Saved	○
Holy	○	Spirit	○	Forgiveness	○
Pray	○	Bible	○	Amen	○
Love	○	Faith	○	Joy	○
Worship	○	Disciples	○	Peace	○

My Favorite Song Today _____

Use this space to mark down things you didn't understand or questions you might have.

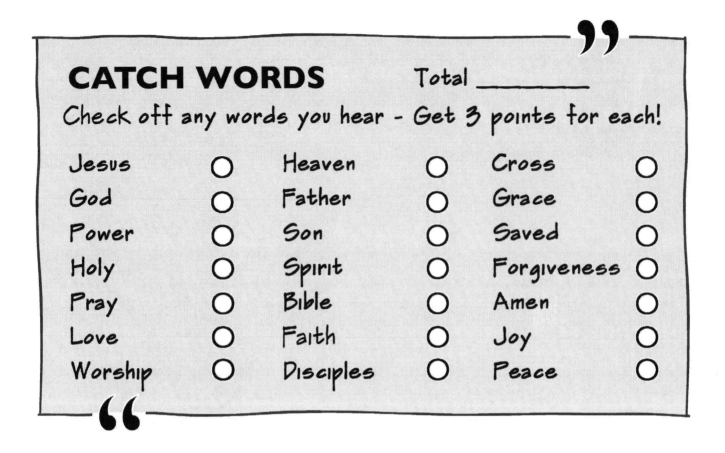

TODAY'S SERMON

Is about...

_____

_____

_____

_____

_____

_____

_____

DATE
_____

Try to get 30 points!

SUNDAY MORNING CHECKLIST

_____ give yourself 5 points for each! _____

I prayed when I woke up this morning ☐

I brushed my teeth ☐

I made my bed ☐

I came to church with a good attitude ☐

I said hello to someone when I arrived ☐

I brought my Bible to church ☐

Total . . . . . . ☐

CATCH WORDS

Total _____

Check off any words you hear - Get 3 points for each!

Jesus	◯	Heaven	◯	Cross	◯
God	◯	Father	◯	Grace	◯
Power	◯	Son	◯	Saved	◯
Holy	◯	Spirit	◯	Forgiveness	◯
Pray	◯	Bible	◯	Amen	◯
Love	◯	Faith	◯	Joy	◯
Worship	◯	Disciples	◯	Peace	◯

My Favorite Song Today _____

_____

_____

_____

Use this space to mark down things you didn't understand or questions you might have.

TODAY'S SERMON

Is about...

_____

_____

_____

_____

_____

_____

_____

DATE

_____

Try to get 30 points!

SUNDAY MORNING CHECKLIST

_____ give yourself 5 points for each! _____

I prayed when I woke up this morning ☐

I brushed my teeth ☐

I made my bed ☐

I came to church with a good attitude ☐

I said hello to someone when I arrived ☐

I brought my Bible to church ☐

Total . . . . . . ☐

CATCH WORDS

Total _____

Check off any words you hear - Get 3 points for each!

Jesus	○	Heaven	○	Cross	○
God	○	Father	○	Grace	○
Power	○	Son	○	Saved	○
Holy	○	Spirit	○	Forgiveness	○
Pray	○	Bible	○	Amen	○
Love	○	Faith	○	Joy	○
Worship	○	Disciples	○	Peace	○

My Favorite Song Today _____

Use this space to mark down things you didn't understand or questions you might have.

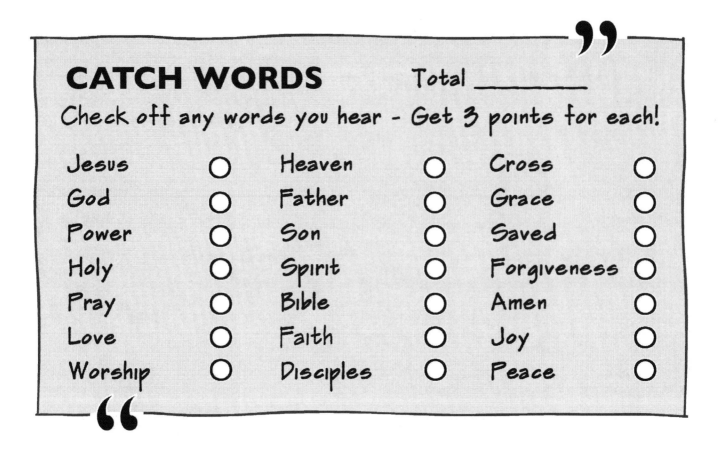

TODAY'S SERMON

Is about...

_____
_____
_____
_____
_____
_____
_____

DATE
_____

Try to get 30 points!

SUNDAY MORNING CHECKLIST

give yourself 5 points for each!

I prayed when I woke up this morning ☐

I brushed my teeth ☐

I made my bed ☐

I came to church with a good attitude ☐

I said hello to someone when I arrived ☐

I brought my Bible to church ☐

Total . . . . . . ☐

CATCH WORDS

Total _____

Check off any words you hear - Get 3 points for each!

Jesus	◯	Heaven	◯	Cross	◯
God	◯	Father	◯	Grace	◯
Power	◯	Son	◯	Saved	◯
Holy	◯	Spirit	◯	Forgiveness	◯
Pray	◯	Bible	◯	Amen	◯
Love	◯	Faith	◯	Joy	◯
Worship	◯	Disciples	◯	Peace	◯

My Favorite Song Today _____

_____

_____

_____

Use this space to mark down things you didn't understand or questions you might have.

smile!

TODAY'S SERMON

Is about...

_____

_____

_____

_____

_____

_____

_____

DATE

_____

Try to get 30 points!

SUNDAY MORNING CHECKLIST

_____ give yourself 5 points for each! _____

I prayed when I woke up this morning ☐

I brushed my teeth ☐

I made my bed ☐

I came to church with a good attitude ☐

I said hello to someone when I arrived ☐

I brought my Bible to church ☐

Total . . . . . . ☐

CATCH WORDS

Total _____

Check off any words you hear - Get 3 points for each!

Jesus	⃝	Heaven	⃝	Cross	⃝
God	⃝	Father	⃝	Grace	⃝
Power	⃝	Son	⃝	Saved	⃝
Holy	⃝	Spirit	⃝	Forgiveness	⃝
Pray	⃝	Bible	⃝	Amen	⃝
Love	⃝	Faith	⃝	Joy	⃝
Worship	⃝	Disciples	⃝	Peace	⃝

My Favorite Song Today _____

Use this space to mark down things you didn't understand or questions you might have.

TODAY'S SERMON

Is about...

_____
_____
_____
_____
_____
_____
_____

DATE

_____

Try to get 30 points!

SUNDAY MORNING CHECKLIST

— give yourself 5 points for each! —

I prayed when I woke up this morning ☐

I brushed my teeth ☐

I made my bed ☐

I came to church with a good attitude ☐

I said hello to someone when I arrived ☐

I brought my Bible to church ☐

Total . . . . . . ☐

CATCH WORDS

Total _____

Check off any words you hear - Get 3 points for each!

Jesus	○	Heaven	○	Cross	○
God	○	Father	○	Grace	○
Power	○	Son	○	Saved	○
Holy	○	Spirit	○	Forgiveness	○
Pray	○	Bible	○	Amen	○
Love	○	Faith	○	Joy	○
Worship	○	Disciples	○	Peace	○

My Favorite Song Today _____

_____
_____
_____

Use this space to mark down things you didn't understand or questions you might have.

TODAY'S SERMON

Is about...

_____
_____
_____
_____
_____
_____
_____

DATE
_____

Try to get 30 points!

SUNDAY MORNING CHECKLIST
_____ give yourself 5 points for each! _____

I prayed when I woke up this morning ☐

I brushed my teeth ☐

I made my bed ☐

I came to church with a good attitude ☐

I said hello to someone when I arrived ☐

I brought my Bible to church ☐

Total . . . . . . ☐

CATCH WORDS

Total _____

Check off any words you hear - Get 3 points for each!

Jesus	◯	Heaven	◯	Cross	◯
God	◯	Father	◯	Grace	◯
Power	◯	Son	◯	Saved	◯
Holy	◯	Spirit	◯	Forgiveness	◯
Pray	◯	Bible	◯	Amen	◯
Love	◯	Faith	◯	Joy	◯
Worship	◯	Disciples	◯	Peace	◯

My Favorite Song Today _____

_____

_____

_____

Use this space to mark down things you didn't understand or questions you might have.

TODAY'S SERMON

Is about...

_____
_____
_____
_____
_____
_____
_____

DATE

_____

Try to get 30 points!

SUNDAY MORNING CHECKLIST

—— give yourself 5 points for each! ——

I prayed when I woke up this morning ☐

I brushed my teeth ☐

I made my bed ☐

I came to church with a good attitude ☐

I said hello to someone when I arrived ☐

I brought my Bible to church ☐

Total . . . . . . ☐

CATCH WORDS

Total _____

Check off any words you hear - Get 3 points for each!

Jesus	◯	Heaven	◯	Cross	◯
God	◯	Father	◯	Grace	◯
Power	◯	Son	◯	Saved	◯
Holy	◯	Spirit	◯	Forgiveness	◯
Pray	◯	Bible	◯	Amen	◯
Love	◯	Faith	◯	Joy	◯
Worship	◯	Disciples	◯	Peace	◯

My Favorite Song Today _____

_____

_____

_____

Use this space to mark down things you didn't understand or questions you might have.

TODAY'S SERMON

Is about...

_____
_____
_____
_____
_____
_____
_____
_____

DATE
_____

Try to get 30 points!

SUNDAY MORNING CHECKLIST

_____ give yourself 5 points for each! _____

I prayed when I woke up this morning ☐

I brushed my teeth ☐

I made my bed ☐

I came to church with a good attitude ☐

I said hello to someone when I arrived ☐

I brought my Bible to church ☐

Total . . . . . . ☐

CATCH WORDS

Total _____

Check off any words you hear - Get 3 points for each!

Jesus	◯	Heaven	◯	Cross	◯
God	◯	Father	◯	Grace	◯
Power	◯	Son	◯	Saved	◯
Holy	◯	Spirit	◯	Forgiveness	◯
Pray	◯	Bible	◯	Amen	◯
Love	◯	Faith	◯	Joy	◯
Worship	◯	Disciples	◯	Peace	◯

My Favorite Song Today _____

Use this space to mark down things you didn't understand or questions you might have.

This Week I'll Pray For...

_____

_____

_____

_____

Did you read your Bible this week?
If you did, give yourself 10 points!

Extra notes
or doodles go
here --->

Tally up
your
points!

TODAY'S SERMON

Is about...

_____
_____
_____
_____
_____
_____
_____

DATE
_____

Try to get 30 points!

SUNDAY MORNING CHECKLIST

_____ give yourself 5 points for each! _____

I prayed when I woke up this morning ☐

I brushed my teeth ☐

I made my bed ☐

I came to church with a good attitude ☐

I said hello to someone when I arrived ☐

I brought my Bible to church ☐

Total . . . . . . ☐

CATCH WORDS

Total _____

Check off any words you hear - Get 3 points for each!

Jesus	○	Heaven	○	Cross	○
God	○	Father	○	Grace	○
Power	○	Son	○	Saved	○
Holy	○	Spirit	○	Forgiveness	○
Pray	○	Bible	○	Amen	○
Love	○	Faith	○	Joy	○
Worship	○	Disciples	○	Peace	○

My Favorite Song Today _____

_____

_____

_____

Use this space to mark down things you didn't understand or questions you might have.

TODAY'S SERMON
Is about...

_____

_____

_____

_____

_____

_____

DATE
_____

Try to get 30 points!

SUNDAY MORNING CHECKLIST
_____ give yourself 5 points for each! _____

I prayed when I woke up this morning ☐

I brushed my teeth ☐

I made my bed ☐

I came to church with a good attitude ☐

I said hello to someone when I arrived ☐

I brought my Bible to church ☐

Total . . . . . . ☐

CATCH WORDS

Total _____

Check off any words you hear - Get 3 points for each!

Jesus	○	Heaven	○	Cross	○
God	○	Father	○	Grace	○
Power	○	Son	○	Saved	○
Holy	○	Spirit	○	Forgiveness	○
Pray	○	Bible	○	Amen	○
Love	○	Faith	○	Joy	○
Worship	○	Disciples	○	Peace	○

My Favorite Song Today _____

Use this space to mark down things you didn't understand or questions you might have.

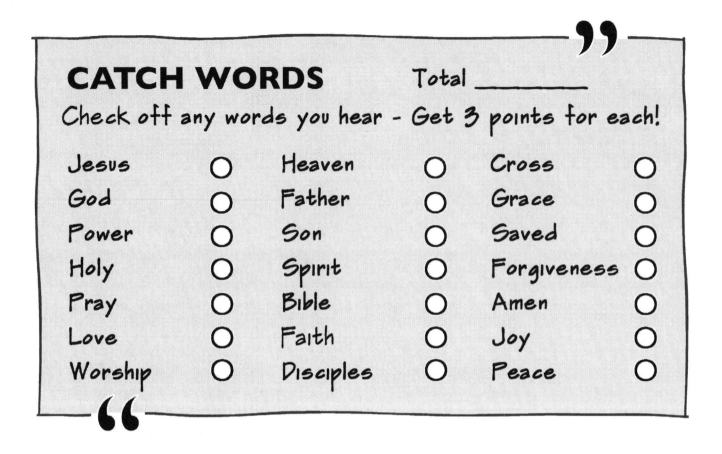

This Week I'll Pray For...

Did you read your Bible this week? If you did, give yourself 10 points!

Extra notes or doodles go here --->

Tally up your points!

TODAY'S SERMON

Is about...

_____

_____

_____

_____

_____

_____

_____

DATE

_____

Try to get 30 points!

SUNDAY MORNING CHECKLIST

_____ give yourself 5 points for each! _____

I prayed when I woke up this morning ☐

I brushed my teeth ☐

I made my bed ☐

I came to church with a good attitude ☐

I said hello to someone when I arrived ☐

I brought my Bible to church ☐

Total . . . . . . ☐

CATCH WORDS

Total _____

Check off any words you hear - Get 3 points for each!

Jesus	○	Heaven	○	Cross	○
God	○	Father	○	Grace	○
Power	○	Son	○	Saved	○
Holy	○	Spirit	○	Forgiveness	○
Pray	○	Bible	○	Amen	○
Love	○	Faith	○	Joy	○
Worship	○	Disciples	○	Peace	○

My Favorite Song Today _____

Use this space to mark down things you didn't understand or questions you might have.

This Week I'll Pray For...

Did you read your Bible this week? If you did, give yourself 10 points!

Extra notes or doodles go here --->

Tally up your points!

TODAY'S SERMON

Is about...

_____

_____

_____

_____

_____

_____

_____

DATE

_____

Try to get 30 points!

SUNDAY MORNING CHECKLIST

_____ give yourself 5 points for each! _____

I prayed when I woke up this morning ☐

I brushed my teeth ☐

I made my bed ☐

I came to church with a good attitude ☐

I said hello to someone when I arrived ☐

I brought my Bible to church ☐

Total . . . . . . ☐

CATCH WORDS

Total _____

Check off any words you hear - Get 3 points for each!

Jesus	○	Heaven	○	Cross	○
God	○	Father	○	Grace	○
Power	○	Son	○	Saved	○
Holy	○	Spirit	○	Forgiveness	○
Pray	○	Bible	○	Amen	○
Love	○	Faith	○	Joy	○
Worship	○	Disciples	○	Peace	○

My Favorite Song Today _____

Use this space to mark down things you didn't understand or questions you might have.

TODAY'S SERMON

Is about...

_____
_____
_____
_____
_____
_____
_____

DATE
_____

Try to get 30 points!

SUNDAY MORNING CHECKLIST

_____ give yourself 5 points for each! _____

I prayed when I woke up this morning ☐

I brushed my teeth ☐

I made my bed ☐

I came to church with a good attitude ☐

I said hello to someone when I arrived ☐

I brought my Bible to church ☐

Total . . . . . . ☐

CATCH WORDS

Total _____

Check off any words you hear - Get 3 points for each!

Jesus	◯	Heaven	◯	Cross	◯
God	◯	Father	◯	Grace	◯
Power	◯	Son	◯	Saved	◯
Holy	◯	Spirit	◯	Forgiveness	◯
Pray	◯	Bible	◯	Amen	◯
Love	◯	Faith	◯	Joy	◯
Worship	◯	Disciples	◯	Peace	◯

My Favorite Song Today _____

_____

_____

_____

Use this space to mark down things you didn't understand or questions you might have.

TODAY'S SERMON

Is about...

_____
_____
_____
_____
_____
_____

DATE
_____

Try to get 30 points!

SUNDAY MORNING CHECKLIST

_____ give yourself 5 points for each! _____

I prayed when I woke up this morning ☐

I brushed my teeth ☐

I made my bed ☐

I came to church with a good attitude ☐

I said hello to someone when I arrived ☐

I brought my Bible to church ☐

Total . . . . . . ☐

CATCH WORDS

Total _____

Check off any words you hear - Get 3 points for each!

Jesus	○	Heaven	○	Cross	○
God	○	Father	○	Grace	○
Power	○	Son	○	Saved	○
Holy	○	Spirit	○	Forgiveness	○
Pray	○	Bible	○	Amen	○
Love	○	Faith	○	Joy	○
Worship	○	Disciples	○	Peace	○

My Favorite Song Today _____

_____

_____

_____

Use this space to mark down things you didn't understand or questions you might have.

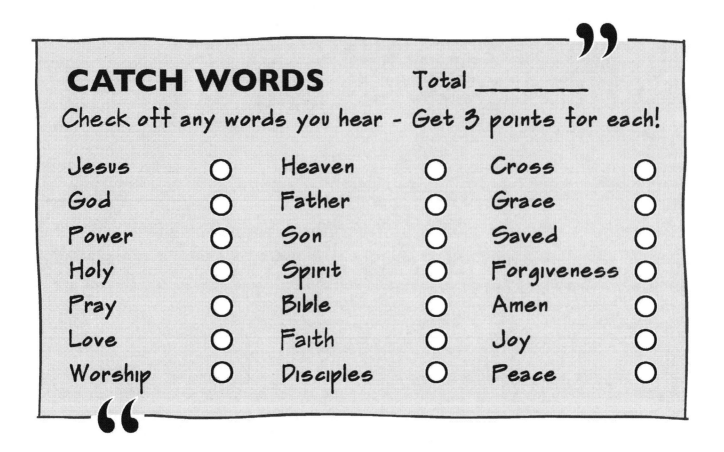

This Week I'll Pray For...

_____

_____

_____

_____

Did you read your Bible this week?
If you did, give yourself 10 points!

Extra notes
or doodles go
here --->

Tally up
your
points!

TODAY'S SERMON

Is about...

_____

_____

_____

_____

_____

_____

_____

DATE
_____

Try to get 30 points!

SUNDAY MORNING CHECKLIST

_____ give yourself 5 points for each! _____

I prayed when I woke up this morning ☐

I brushed my teeth ☐

I made my bed ☐

I came to church with a good attitude ☐

I said hello to someone when I arrived ☐

I brought my Bible to church ☐

Total . . . . . . ☐

CATCH WORDS

Total _____

Check off any words you hear - Get 3 points for each!

Jesus	◯	Heaven	◯	Cross	◯
God	◯	Father	◯	Grace	◯
Power	◯	Son	◯	Saved	◯
Holy	◯	Spirit	◯	Forgiveness	◯
Pray	◯	Bible	◯	Amen	◯
Love	◯	Faith	◯	Joy	◯
Worship	◯	Disciples	◯	Peace	◯

My Favorite Song Today _____

_____

_____

_____

Use this space to mark down things you didn't understand or questions you might have.

TODAY'S SERMON

Is about...

_____
_____
_____
_____
_____
_____
_____

DATE
_____

Try to get 30 points!

SUNDAY MORNING CHECKLIST

_____ give yourself 5 points for each! _____

I prayed when I woke up this morning ☐

I brushed my teeth ☐

I made my bed ☐

I came to church with a good attitude ☐

I said hello to someone when I arrived ☐

I brought my Bible to church ☐

Total . . . . . . ☐

CATCH WORDS

Total _____

Check off any words you hear - Get 3 points for each!

Jesus	○	Heaven	○	Cross	○
God	○	Father	○	Grace	○
Power	○	Son	○	Saved	○
Holy	○	Spirit	○	Forgiveness	○
Pray	○	Bible	○	Amen	○
Love	○	Faith	○	Joy	○
Worship	○	Disciples	○	Peace	○

My Favorite Song Today _____

Use this space to mark down things you didn't understand or questions you might have.

TODAY'S SERMON

Is about...

_____

_____

_____

_____

_____

_____

_____

DATE

_____

Try to get 30 points!

SUNDAY MORNING CHECKLIST

_____ give yourself 5 points for each! _____

I prayed when I woke up this morning ☐

I brushed my teeth ☐

I made my bed ☐

I came to church with a good attitude ☐

I said hello to someone when I arrived ☐

I brought my Bible to church ☐

Total . . . . . . ☐

CATCH WORDS
Total _____

Check off any words you hear - Get 3 points for each!

Jesus	○	Heaven	○	Cross	○
God	○	Father	○	Grace	○
Power	○	Son	○	Saved	○
Holy	○	Spirit	○	Forgiveness	○
Pray	○	Bible	○	Amen	○
Love	○	Faith	○	Joy	○
Worship	○	Disciples	○	Peace	○

My Favorite Song Today _____

_____

_____

_____

Use this space to mark down things you didn't understand or questions you might have.

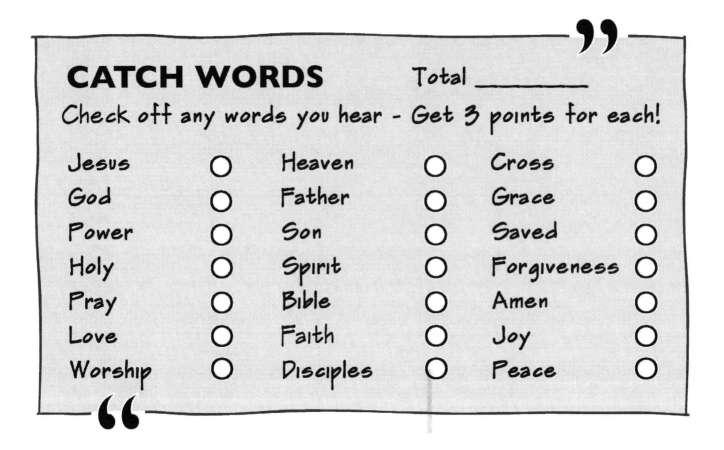

This Week I'll Pray For...

_____

_____

_____

_____

Did you read your Bible this week?
If you did, give yourself 10 points!

Extra notes
or doodles go
here --->

Tally up
your
points!

TODAY'S SERMON
Is about...

_____
_____
_____
_____
_____
_____
_____

DATE
_____

Try to get 30 points!

SUNDAY MORNING CHECKLIST
_____ give yourself 5 points for each! _____

I prayed when I woke up this morning ☐

I brushed my teeth ☐

I made my bed ☐

I came to church with a good attitude ☐

I said hello to someone when I arrived ☐

I brought my Bible to church ☐

Total . . . . . . ☐

CATCH WORDS

Total _____

Check off any words you hear - Get 3 points for each!

Jesus	◯	Heaven	◯	Cross	◯
God	◯	Father	◯	Grace	◯
Power	◯	Son	◯	Saved	◯
Holy	◯	Spirit	◯	Forgiveness	◯
Pray	◯	Bible	◯	Amen	◯
Love	◯	Faith	◯	Joy	◯
Worship	◯	Disciples	◯	Peace	◯

My Favorite Song Today _____

_____

_____

_____

Use this space to mark down things you didn't understand or questions you might have.

About the Author:

After two years as a social media assistant, Madison Schacht makes her debut in the book industry. Her creativity, and outstanding eye for design is what separates her from the crowd.

With a love for Jesus and passion for music, she ministers on the worship team at her church.

About the Author:

Darlene Schacht is known by her readers as The Time-Warp Wife. She is an Evangelical Christian whose number one priority is to serve Jesus Christ in every area of her life. She and her husband Michael live in Manitoba Canada. Married 26 years, they have four children (three still at home) and a pug.

She's an award winning and New York Times best-selling author.

Find Darlene on the web here:

Blog: TimeWarpWife.com Facebook: timewarpwife

Twitter: timewarpwife   Pinterest: timewarpwife

If you enjoyed this book, please leave a review at Amazon. Thank you!